O9-BRZ-768

THE BOOK OF REPTILES AND AMPHIBIANS

The Book of

REPTILES

Written and Illustrated by

Doubleday & Company, Inc., Garden City, N. Y.

and AMPHIBIANS

MICHAEL H. BEVANS

Library of Congress Catalog Card Number 55-9715

Printed in the United States of America

TABLE OF CONTENTS

INTRODUCTION

The United States has a great variety and abundance of wild animals, but many of these are of small to medium size and have secretive habits and so are not familiar to most people. Prominent among such creatures are the reptiles and the amphibians, which may be divided into six main groups, thus: The term *reptiles* includes snakes, lizards, turtles, and crocodilians, while *amphibians* covers frogs-and-toads and salamanders.

These animals have a most interesting history, for they represent a "link" between the fishes and what are called the higher animals. The amphibians of old are reputed to have been the pioneers of animal life on the shore and the ancestors of all reptiles, birds, and mammals. Present-day examples of this group (frogs, toads, and salamanders) are still very dependent on water for survival and need considerable moisture for their delicate, scaleless skins. They lay their fish-like eggs in water and have larval young (called tadpoles or polliwogs) that possess tail fins and "breathe" with gills.

Reptiles, as first-comers on dry land, were enormously successful and at one time virtually ruled the earth. Giant species we call dinosaurs roamed the plains and savannas and some even invaded the sea again. For some reason most of these older types died off altogether, leaving only the turtles, crocodiles, and alligators to survive in nearly their original form, but still another branch of the reptile family gave rise to the snakes and lizards of today. All of these reptilian survivors have a body covering of scales or "shields" and breathe with lungs throughout their lives. Some lay eggs similar to birds' eggs and some bear living young, but in either case the babies are miniatures of their parents.

One particular trait the reptiles and amphibians share in common is that they do not have a constant body warmth. By moving into sun or shade or retreating underground they must manage to keep from getting too hot or too cold, and in severe weather they usually become torpid and retire to some place of uniform, moderate temperature. In the winter cold this is called *hibernation*, while similar escape from summer heat is called *aestivation*. Temperature regulates the whole life of these animals.

It would be nice if one could introduce separately the snakes, the turtles, frogs, and the others, but space does not permit, so general information about each group has been distributed among the texts of various species. However, some mention of the strange legends told about certain of these "critters" may prove amusing.

Snakes in particular seem to stir the human imagination until their true nature is often obscured by myths. One story is that, when frightened, a female snake will open its mouth and her two dozen or more "children" will run down her throat, then crawl out later when danger is past. This is apparently pure fiction, for snakes do not look after their babies and the small ones would shortly suffocate inside. Another story insists that some snakes have a stinger in their tails with a poison powerful enough to "split a hoe handle" or kill a mule! Actually, no known snake has any sort of stinger in its tail, and the chances of one being discovered are small indeed! And so it goes. The fact is that snakes are highly developed vertebrate creatures with basically the same sort of spinal and organic structures as a bird or a cat, but formed in a long, narrow shape. Many kinds (including rattlesnakes) feed almost exclusively on rodents and thus serve as valuable guardians of farm crops.

While some of our snakes have a poisonous bite, a *far* greater number have not, and a diagram is included here to show their respective head structures. Although all snakes have teeth to hold their prey, only a few have specialized fangs, like curved hypodermic needles, and venom to inject as they bite. This is mainly a food-getting apparatus used to kill mice and rats and other prey and has no connection with the harmless forked tongue. For the rare occasions when people are bitten by venomous snakes there are standard procedures to follow which may be learned through a first-aid course, a doctor, or Scout manual.

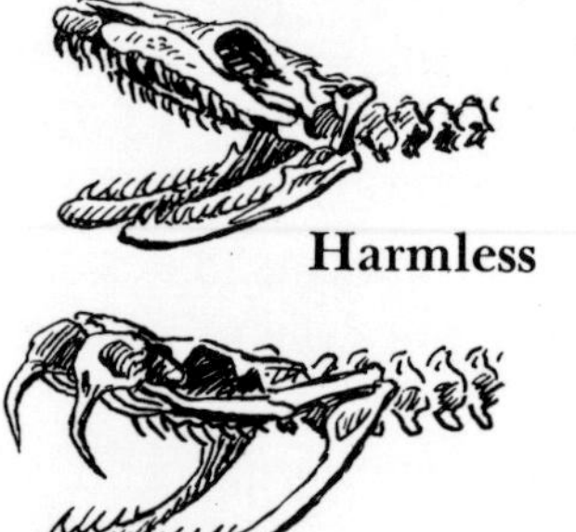

Harmless

Venomous

The lizard and turtle sections are largely self-explanatory, but some mention should be made of the American crocodile. This species (*Crocodilus acutus*, it is called) has been omitted because it occurs in the United States only along a small strip of the south Florida coast and is seen by very few people indeed. A sketch comparing the heads of this reptile and the alligator will distinguish them.

Although the frogs and toads have received a just share of space, we have somewhat slighted the salamanders because so many of them live such extremely secretive lives in remote habitats that they are rarely seen by humans.

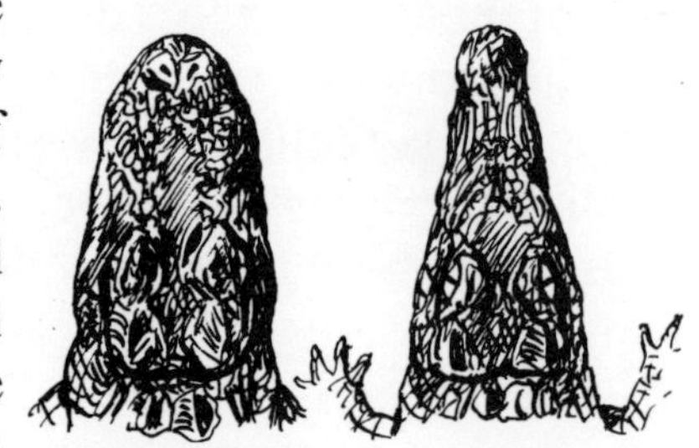

Alligator **Crocodile**

This map is designed to indicate in broad terms the "Habitat Zones" in the United States. Although these zones (represented by areas of color) are often not sharply defined and much is still to be learned about them, they convey a better general idea of where different animals and plants occur than do state lines and long descriptions.

In the description of each species, mention is usually made of part or parts of the country where it lives, such as "Coastal Plain," "Prairie," or "Desert." By referring to this map the reader may gain an understanding of the "range" of each species or group.

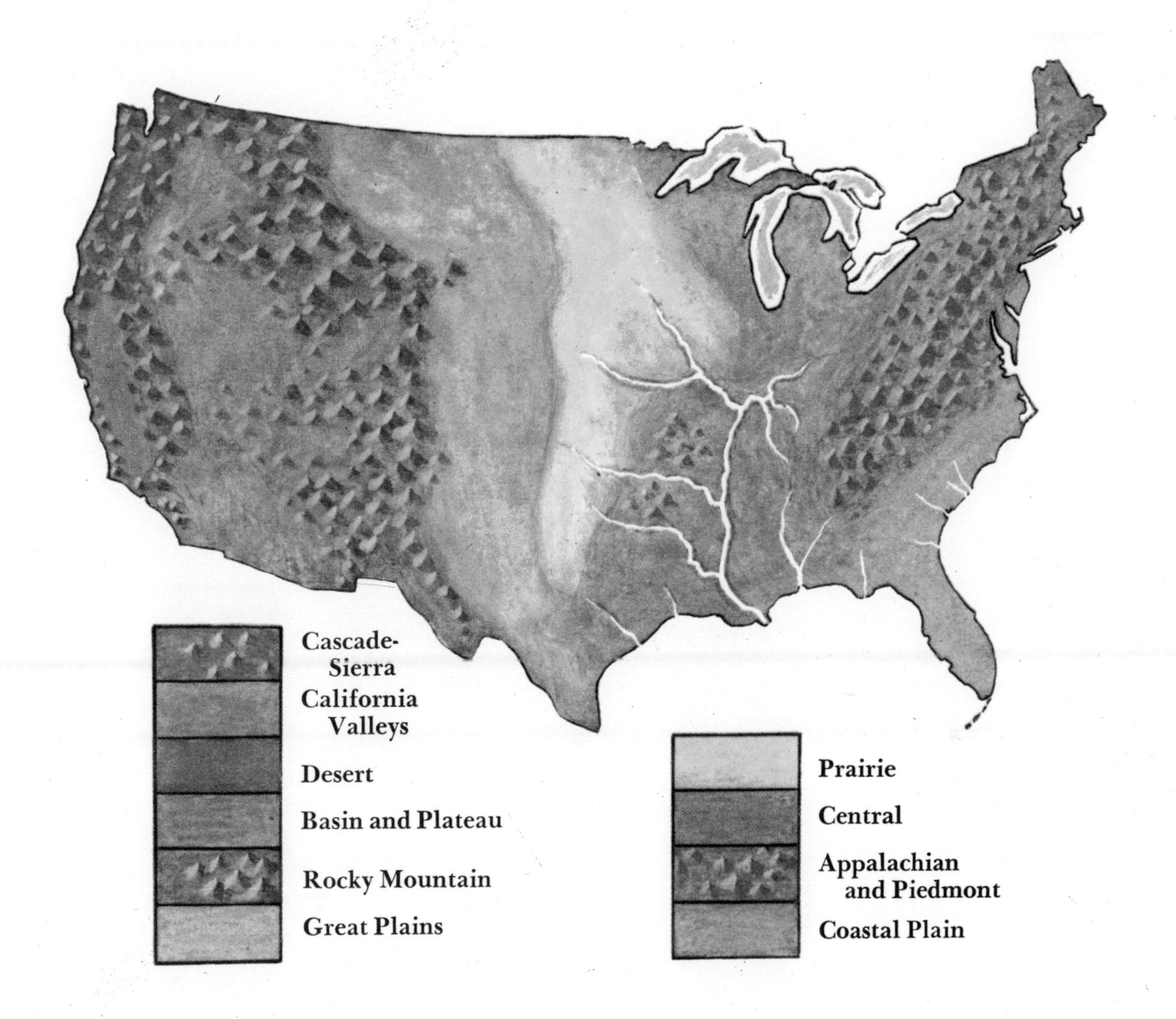

I wish to thank Carl F. Kauffeld, Curator of Reptiles at the Staten Island Zoo, for his professional attention in reviewing this text and for his guidance, in past years, of my early interest in herpetology.

To the young person interested in the world of living things parental tolerance and even encouragement are important. I was most fortunate in this respect and in addition my wife, Jeanne, is an enthusiastic student of all natural phenomena. She has typed the foregoing text, helped immensely with the research and made many valuable suggestions.

THE BOOK OF REPTILES AND AMPHIBIANS

Reptiles: Venomous Snakes

Eastern Diamondback Rattlesnake

Crotalus adamanteus

Some people are afraid of all snakes, but the only sound reason for fearing any of them is that some are poisonous. For safety and peace of mind one should learn to recognize the venomous kinds. Only 39 of our 273 species and subspecies of snakes have a highly developed poison apparatus, and the majority of these are rattlesnakes. Several of the larger rattlers must be considered extremely dangerous to man.

The spectacular eastern diamondback rattler averages about 5 feet when adult. One has been recorded at 8 feet 2 inches long. It is a massive snake, but in spite of its great size wild specimens are usually shy and retiring and their crisscross markings make them very inconspicuous among the shadows of the thickets they so often inhabit. However, an aroused specimen is an awesome sight. The sudden, rasping buzz of the rattle, the massive coil of body, and the glittering dark eyes foretell the latent danger of inch-long fangs and lethal venom that may come with a flashing stroke. The sensitive black forked tongue tests the air to anticipate an opponent's next move, but the snake will often seek the first opportunity to escape into a nearby hole or windfall.

Rabbits seem to be the chief food of these snakes when adult. The 6 to 22 young are born alive and, like all the rattlers and moccasins, are equipped at birth with fangs and venom to kill their own prey. The eastern diamondbacks occur only in the Coastal Plain region from North Carolina to the Mississippi.

Western Diamondback

Crotalus atrox

Like paler, sandy-colored editions of the big eastern diamondback, these husky rattlesnakes may grow to be as large, but the average adult length is somewhat smaller, usually 4 to 5 feet. Their disposition is more pugnacious and "salty," and an angry specimen will often strike at its adversary three or four times in rapid succession. Although they are rarely able to reach more than half their length, each of these repeated efforts can slide the snake forward a bit, thus increasing its range. Many of the snakebite fatalities in the United States are traced to this species, which occurs through most of the southwestern quarter of the country. Their food consists largely of rabbits, gophers, and other rodents.

Sidewinder: Horned Rattler

Crotalus cerastes

These little rattlesnakes, seldom over 20 inches long, are strictly denizens of the southwestern Desert and differ from others of the group in three respects: the hornlike scales above their eyes, the habit of burying themselves in loose sand, and their sidewinding gait, which gets them over soft, shifting sand better than the more usual snake motion. This "sidewinding" is almost impossible to describe but could be likened to the action of a short rope held by one end and flipped across the ground with circular wrist motions. During this progress the snake's head points at right angles to the direction he is traveling!

Sidewinders prowl almost exclusively at night and feed on lizards and mice.

The Massasaugas

Sistrurus catenatus

The massasaugas, so called by the Indians, and the pigmy rattlers, *S. miliarius*, belong to a different group from the "true" rattlesnakes. They have longish tails, small rattles, and head scalation more like the moccasins. The massasaugas, which are sometimes uniform black, occur from western New York to Arizona, while the three varieties of pigmy rattlers live in the southern Coastal Plain.

Although neither of these snakes averages much over 2 feet in length (the pigmies even less than this), their bite can be painful and dangerous.

The Copperheads

Ancistrodon contortrix

"Highland moccasin" is another name for these snakes that well indicates their likeness to the cottonmouth or water moccasin. The flat-topped, angular snout, the catlike pupils, and the distinctive markings and colors should prevent one from confusing a copperhead with harmless species. Generally these snakes are shy and frequently they lie among dead leaves that blend very nicely with their hues, thus escaping detection altogether. This surely helps the snakes to catch their food of unwary mice or frogs, but people, too, are sometimes bitten because they don't see them and may accidentally touch or step on a copperhead. The bite is a serious matter indeed but rarely fatal to human adults.

The northern copperhead (below, right) usually inhabits rocky forest margins in the Appalachian, Piedmont and Central areas, and dozens of them often "den up" in winter with timber rattlers and pilot black snakes. They average well under 3 feet long, and the females bear three to nine young alive in late summer. The southern copperhead (below, left) and the two western copperheads differ mainly in color and shape of the crossband markings. No copperheads occur west of the Rockies or on the northern plains.

The Timber Rattlesnakes

Crotalus horridus

The timber or banded rattlesnake occurs over the eastern half of the United States with the exception of the Florida peninsula, Delmarva Peninsula, and extreme northern parts of New England and the Great Lakes. The typical northern variety may be yellow or black, as shown here, or may be of intermediate colors. It usually prefers uninhabited rocky highlands and is a rather timid snake unless cornered. A southern subspecies, the canebrake rattlesnake, lives in the Coastal Plain and is colored a pinkish brown with narrower black cross-bands and a rusty stripe down its back. A bite from one of these snakes may kill an adult person.

Three to 4 feet is the usual length of breeding-age timber rattlesnakes but, like all reptiles, they continue growing slowly until death. Specimens over 5 feet have been recorded, and the canebrake rattler may grow to over 6 feet, but it is difficult to determine the age of these big fellows. The rattle is of no help because one or several rattle segments may be formed during each year. Only if the rattle tapers and still has the infant snake's "button" on the end (see illustration) can one make a rough estimate of its age.

The yellow specimen shown is part way through the process of shedding its skin, a function that all snakes perform several times a year. A new "outer" layer first forms beneath, followed by a period when the old skin is becoming separated from the new and the whole snake has a dull or milky appearance, especially over the eyes. This is most noticeable a week or so before shedding. When the skin has fully cleared, the snake carefully peels back the old skin from its jaws and, by catching it on some rough surface, crawls slowly out of the old covering. This leaves behind the tissue-like cast-off skin, which is an inside-out copy of the snake's scalation, transparent eye-coverings and all.

Pacific Rattlesnakes

These members of the prairie rattler group are *the* common rattlesnake throughout many far western areas. It inhabits forests, slopes, and valleys and shows much variety in color and markings. Size and venomous qualities are about equal to the prairie race.

Among the many southwestern rattlers for which we do not have room, the desert-dwelling speckled and Panamint Rattlesnakes (*C. mitchelli*) should be mentioned. These forms have remarkably beautiful pale colors and dispositions which (to quote Mr. Kipling) are "all 'ot sand and ginger" when the snakes are disturbed.

Prairie Rattlesnakes

Crotalus viridis ssp.

Probably no rattlers in the United States are more abundant than these reptiles of the Great Plains area. They range from Canada to Mexico and have seven or eight "cousins" (subspecies) which live in the mountain, canyon, and coastal forest regions farther west.

Generally the prairie rattlesnake is a sharp-tempered character, but because of its rather small head, shorter fangs, and lesser total size it can hardly be considered as dangerous as the burly diamondback. It is quite certainly of value to farmers in helping to keep down the numbers of gophers and grain-eating rodents, but nonetheless a great many of these snakes are killed yearly by people who find their winter denning place and slaughter them when they come out in the spring. The usual length of the adult snakes is between 3 and 4 feet.

Cottonmouth: Water Moccasin

Ancistrodon piscivorous

This is our only poisonous water snake and is closely related to the copperhead. The water moccasin has earned its name of "cottonmouth" through a peculiar habit of opening its mouth wide and revealing the light-colored interior when frightened and cornered. This trick is accompanied by a tilting back of the head and seems to be a threat or warning. And rightly so, for the gaping is frequently followed by a lightning-quick, stabbing stroke in which the curved, erectile fangs are plunged into the enemy. Sometimes this flash of action comes very unexpectedly, for these snakes appear rather sluggish in habits.

The average length of adult cottonmouths is about 3½ feet, but in some regions 5-footers are not uncommon. At any size they are proportionately stout snakes, but the babies, which are born alive in the late summer, have sharply outlined brick-red markings quite unlike their dull-colored parents and more like copperheads. Although two varieties of cottonmouths are recognized (an eastern form and a darker, Gulf drainage phase), they are strictly southern Coastal Plain snakes with northernmost limits in southern Illinois and southeastern Virginia.

The cottonmouth shares the southern swamplands with several kinds of harmless water snakes, some of which are tough-looking with wide, lumpy heads and dispositions to match, but still not poisonous. A particularly handy way to identify a real cottonmouth is to note the shape of its head, the flat-topped snout with "square" edges, and the arrogant, scowling expression that is quite different from the rounded-off nose and bug-eyed stare of the nonvenomous species. Other cottonmouth features are the loreal pits, elliptical pupils, and a single row of plates under the tail. Although these snakes prefer water margins and will swim to escape or to catch fish and frogs, they do wander on land and will also eat rodents, insects, and other snakes. The bite of a cottonmouth is a very serious matter, requiring all available treatment.

The Coral Snakes

Micrurus and *Micruroides*

Coral snakes belong to an entirely different family from our other poisonous forms (they are related to the cobras) and don't look really dangerous at all. Like many bright-colored, highly "polished" snakes, they live below ground, under logs or leaf mulch. Two types occur here. The common coral snake, *Micrurus* shown above, inhabits the Coastal Plain, and the Sonoran coral snake, *Micruroides*, southern Arizona and New Mexico. Both of these have a different arrangement of red, black, and yellow markings from the harmless snakes that resemble them (p. 23).

Their venom, which serves to subdue the lizards and small snakes they feed on, is such a violent nerve poison that a person bitten by a coral snake will rapidly become ill and is quite apt to die. Fortunately their fangs are very short, so the greatest danger lies in placing bare hands or feet on one. Adult corals are about 2 feet long, but maximum for the eastern species is 40 inches. They reproduce by laying eggs.

Reptiles: Mildly Venomous Snakes

Rear-fanged Snakes

Trimorphodon and *Tantilla*

Tantilla **Lyre Snake**

A few of our snakes are mildly poisonous; that is, their bite may cause swelling or pain but is not deadly in its effect on man. They are chiefly small species with gentle dispositions, the only larger ones like the lyre snakes occurring in the extreme Southwest along the U.S.-Mexico border. The several types are generally referred to as rear-fanged snakes.

The lyre snakes, *Trimorphodon*, may attain 3½ feet, but the tiny burrowers called *Tantillas* are rarely more than 9 inches long.

Reptiles: Harmless Snakes

Red Milk Snake

Western Coral King Snake

The Milk Snakes; House Snakes

Lampropeltis doliata

Harmless snakes far outnumber the dangerous species, but many of these non venomous ones are killed by people who mistakenly believe them to be venomous or destructive. The milk snakes, of which there are several varieties, are good examples of this. The common milk snake (shown below) is somehow often mistaken for the copperhead, while the red milk snake and coral king snake (above) are sometimes confused with the really poisonous coral snake shown on the preceding page.

The name "milk snake" comes from the strange and incorrect belief held by some people that these reptiles will climb a cow's leg and take milk from the udders! Even if a cow would stand for this, the snake could drink only a few ounces, not enough to be noticed in the daily milking. The fact is, these are actually smallish king snakes related to those on the opposite page, and the reason they are found around farms is because milk snakes are great mouse eaters. Although occasionally small birds, other snakes, or even insects may be eaten by them, rodents form the bulk of their yearly diet.

In the Northeast, through most of the Appalachian, Piedmont, and Central areas, the common milk snake is found. It is one of the larger members of this group and may grow to 3½ feet in length. Farmers sometimes call it the "checkered adder." In the Coastal Plain, Prairie, and Great Plains differently marked red milk snakes occur, while in the extreme southwestern quarter of the country these are replaced by the western coral kings (upper right, *L. zonata ssp.*).

Like all the king snakes, the milk snakes kill most of their prey by constriction before eating it. This is described on the following page. Again, like the other kings, they lay eggs, usually about a dozen, which are deposited in the late spring or early summer. The hatchlings look much like baby blacksnakes.

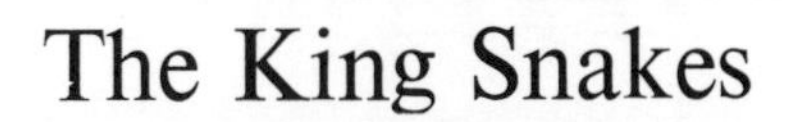

The King Snakes

Lampropeltis getulus

Probably no other American snakes enjoy greater tolerance from human beings than king snakes. This is due to the snake-killing habits of the king snakes which have been somewhat exaggerated. Few people realize that mice and gophers form the larger part of this species' diet. They are constrictors, like many other snakes throughout the world.

Constriction is a means of holding and subduing prey and is usually preceded by a careful stalking of some animal of a suitable sort and size to be eaten. When near enough, the constrictor strikes out suddenly, grasping the other creature with its jaws, and throws one or more coils of its neck and body around the victim. This first move may take less than a second, and almost before it is completed the muscular coils tighten and squeeze. The prey may bite or struggle, but the constant pressure on the sides of its body results in unconsciousness and death, usually from suffocation and heart compression. This may take barely a minute with a small mammal; or with another snake, it may take several hours. The constrictor, having made sure its victim is properly subdued, proceeds to swallow the food at leisure.

Larger king snakes like the eastern variety (upper right) occur from New Jersey to Florida. They may exceed 5 feet in length and can handle quite large opponents, including native venomous snakes, for they seem quite immune to the poison. The speckled king snakes of the central Coastal Plain, southern Prairie, and Great Plains districts average somewhat smaller, while the ringed (or sometimes striped) California and Desert king snakes are rarely over 3 feet long.

The Pine Snakes

Pituophis melenoleucus

Sandy pine flatwoods and scrub oak are the home of these large and powerful snakes. They share, with the western bull snakes, the honor of being among the few snakes who can really "sound off," for both of these reptiles have a structure in the mouth which causes a loud hissing sound when they exhale with force. An angry and cornered pine snake can make quite a fearsome spectacle as he rages, hisses, and strikes, and he often succeeds in scaring off his enemies.

Actually the pine snakes, like most others, prefer a peaceful escape in spite of their size and strength. Average size of the adults seems to be about 5 feet, but specimens over 7 feet have been caught. They feed on mice, rats, squirrels, and occasionally on young rabbits and birds.

The range of these snakes extends from New Jersey to Louisiana, mostly in the Coastal Plain region, and considerable variety in their colors and markings occurs. Northern specimens are usually black and white, those from Florida rusty brown and tan, while one variety from Alabama is totally black. However, the rather small, pointed head, keen eyes, and quite rough scalation are typical of all.

This species is in my opinion more intelligent than most snakes. A female, when preparing a place to deposit her eggs, shows considerable skill in digging with her snout and moving the sand about with her neck and body, and the babies are very able in concealing themselves. They are seldom caught by collectors.

The Bull Snakes: Gopher Snakes

Pituophis catenifer

The bull snakes are western relatives of the pine snakes (opposite) and, like them, are able to produce a loud hissing, roaring sound when angry. Although snakes generally are of great help to farmers because they eat rodents, the bull and gopher snakes have been considered especially valuable in destroying the pestiferous pocket gophers which plague the grain-belt areas. They are adept at pursuing the rodents in underground burrows where no traps would ever reach.

These snakes occur from the Prairie regions of Indiana and Texas to the Pacific coast and into both Canada and Mexico. Of the six varieties that live in this area, those of the Far West are usually called gopher snakes and measure about 4 to 5 feet long when adult. The bull snakes of the Great Plains average 8 to 10 inches longer and may occasionally attain more than 7 feet. All six varieties exhibit yellow, straw, or sand colors with blotches and spots of rust, brown, or black.

The Fox Snake

Elaphe vulpina

Many snakes have well-developed scent glands at the base of the tail which produce an odor when the reptiles are frightened or hurt. The scent of this species is said to resemble that of a fox. People who find these snakes in the wild often confuse them with other species, such as hog-nosed snakes, milk snakes, and even with the massasauga. Actually the fox snake is distinct from all of these and belongs to a large group known as the rat snakes *Elaphe*.

It is a midwestern form that occurs in the north-central and Prairie regions from Nebraska to the Great Lakes.

Black Rat Snake; Pilot Black Snake

Elaphe obsoleta

These snakes may be easily distinguished from the common black racer by their white markings beneath, their rather flat, squarish heads, and shiny, tar-black color. They are more sluggish than the common blacksnake, more powerful and far better climbers. In fact, people often don't know when the rat snakes are in an area because they may be up in a tree or hiding under logs or debris, and frequently they hunt only at night. Fortunately they are entirely harmless to people and of great value in keeping the rat, mouse, and squirrel populations in check, for they have enormous appetites.

The rat snakes (scientists call this group *Elaphes*) kill their prey by constriction and all are egg-layers, usually choosing rotted wood pulp as a nesting site. There are indications that the parents guard their eggs and aid in incubation.

The pilot black snakes, so called because they were thought to "lead the rattlesnakes to safety," are among the longest harmless native snakes in the United States. One was caught which measured 8 feet 5 inches, though the average adult measures nearer 5 feet. Several color varieties of this snake or species closely related to it include the gray rat snake, Texas rat snake, and the striped chicken snake, all of the Coastal Plain. The pilot or mountain black is largely a highland form of the Appalachian and Central areas, although its young are colored like the southern gray rat snake.

Yellow Rat Snake: Striped Chicken Snake

Elaphe o. quadrivittata

Climbing seems to be a specialty of these snakes. Occasionally they enter chicken houses in search of the rodents that often abound there and, during their visit, may eat a couple of eggs or a young chicken, hence one common name. Experts generally agree that the rats and mice eaten by them more than make up for any losses to the farmer.

The adult striped chicken snake may be dark olive to golden yellow, but the young are marked much like baby pilot black snakes, for this is a color variety of the latter. Range is the Coastal Plain from Cape Henry, North Carolina, down through the Florida Keys.

The Corn Snake

Elaphe guttata

Few snakes get more compliments from human observers than the corn snake or red rat snake. It has a rather small slender head and a particularly beautiful coloration, but in spite of this appearance of delicacy it is (like the other *Elaphes*) a powerful constrictor and a fierce enemy of all smaller rodents. In a wild state this snake frequently inhabits cultivated fields and outbuildings and has very secretive, night-prowling habits. Average adult length is 3 to 4 feet, but one 6-footer is on record.

This red form occurs from southern New Jersey to the Mississippi and is most abundant in the Coastal Plain. A gray and brown subspecies (the Great Plains rat snake, *E. g. emoryi*) replaces it farther west and ranges beyond the Rockies and into Mexico.

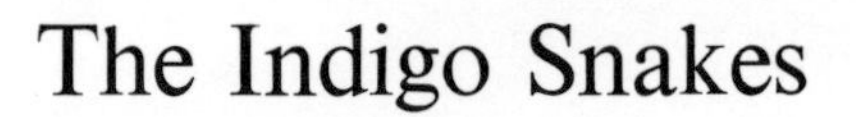

The Indigo Snakes

Drymarchon corais

No other harmless snake in the United States attains a greater average size than the big indigo. About 8 feet seems to be the record, but 6-footers are not uncommon. It is quite stout-bodied for a fast-moving "racer" type. Although the indigo snake often uses a loop of its body to hold down an animal it is eating, it does not constrict its prey. The food includes mice, rats, gophers (it is sometimes called gopher snake), frogs, fish, other snakes, and lizards.

These snakes are usually very good-natured and although quite highstrung will tolerate handling so well that carnival snake "charmers" often use them for exhibit. Because of this demand for indigo snakes and because large specimens are also hunted by skin collectors for making fancy shoes, this handsome species has probably been quite reduced in numbers.

The indigo shown here, *D. c. couperi*, occurs in the Coastal Plain from South Carolina through Florida to the Mississippi, but another subspecies, *D. c. erebennus*, with orange and brown on the head and forebody lives in south Texas and Mexico.

One peculiarity of the indigo is a rounded ridge up the back (even when the snake is well fed) and a habit of flattening the neck *vertically* when badly frightened or angry. It also has a considerable degree of immunity to the venom of native poisonous snakes upon which it sometimes feeds. Baby indigo snakes are rarely seen and little is known of the breeding or nesting habits. The eggs, as large as hens' eggs but more elongated, are covered with coarse grains like calcium salt.

The Coachwhip Snakes

Masticophis flagellum

Whipsnakes of several kinds occur in the United States, but the only species with a coast-to-coast range is the coachwhip snake. Reddish, gray, and black varieties occur across the southern half of the country, but the eastern form shown here is the largest member of the group. It may grow to over 8 feet in length, though the average is nearer 5.

The name "coachwhip" comes from the slim tapered form and the scales which resemble the surface of a braided whip. These reptiles are among the fastest of all snakes, even on open ground, and the speed with which they can travel in a thicket is amazing. Twigs and shrubbery give a snake's body something to push against and actually aid its progress. Whipsnakes usually inhabit rather open, sandy country and are quick to spot human intruders and dash into the nearest clump of bushes. Easily frightened and angered, these reptiles have temperaments as nervous as birds. Their food includes mice, lizards, small birds, and other snakes.

Generally whipsnakes choose proportionately small creatures to eat, for the prey often struggles and bites during this process and they do not have the advantage of venom, constriction, or weight possessed by some snakes. All snakes, of course, have a delicately formed and loosely connected bony structure of the head which allows them with the aid of their recurved teeth, virtually to "walk" their jaws over the captured prey. The skin of the neck and throat stretches to accommodate the food. Naturally, if the food animal has been killed or rendered helpless first, this is much easier.

The coachwhip, like all our racers and whipsnakes, is an egg-laying species.

Blacksnake; Blue Racer

Coluber constrictor

The racers are high-strung, fast-moving snakes of rather slender form. They have proportionately long tails and dark, hawk-like eyes and occur from coast to coast. All of the seven varieties appear to be color phases of one species, the most familiar of these being the common blacksnake or black racer of the East, and the blue, yellow-bellied, or green racers of the West.

Blacksnakes or blue racers are quite often seen by people because they inhabit all sorts of country and move about freely in the daytime but are seldom caught because at the first sign of danger they usually dash off through the underbrush or into a hole. Many yarns are told about these snakes, some true, some false. The most common one is that blacksnakes will attack people. This is partly true, for in the spring mating season, when several may be together around the rocky ledges or thickets where they hibernate, a blacksnake will sometimes advance toward a person with its mouth open in a threatening manner and may strike frantically at the intruder. If a person is bitten, the resulting scratches should be treated like any minor abrasion.

Although given the technical name of *constrictor* (a mistake by Linnaeus, who possibly confused this with the pilot black snake), these racers eat by seizing their prey of insects, mice, frogs, lizards, or small snakes and birds, and swallowing it alive. They have no power to "charm" birds, as is often contended.

The eggs, which have a rough, granular surface, are usually laid in a clutch of one to two dozen in moist debris or under a large stone in early summer. The spotted hatchlings are about 9 inches long. The adults average 4 feet but may reach nearly 6.

Mud Snake: "Hoop" Snake

Farancia abacura

Here is another snake that is predominantly black, but it is the only species that has a vivid, pink-red belly color that reaches up the sides. It is a burrowing snake and spends much of its life prowling in the mud and shallow water of swamp margins, searching for the eel-like salamanders (*Siren* and *Amphiuma*) that are its main article of diet. Adult specimens vary from 3½ to 6 feet in length.

Mud snakes often rest in a circular coil, and from this habit people may have imagined the "hoop snake" story. (This legend has it that the hoop snake takes tail in mouth and rolls down a hill.) Another myth, the one about "a-snake-with-a-stinger-in-its-tail," can also be traced to this species. Frightened mud snakes may hide their heads and jerk the thick, sharp-pointed tails about in a way calculated to startle the uninitiated. Actually the pointed tip is as harmless as the end of a sharp pencil.

These snakes occur only in Coastal Plain regions.

Worm Snake

Carphophis amoena

Eight or 9 inches seems to be the usual adult size of these little burrowers. Not only do they resemble earthworms, but to a large extent they feed on them. Like the mud snakes, they are egg-layers and have a similar polished scalation, tiny eyes, and sharp, abruptly pointed tails. They occur east of the Great Plains in areas of abundant leaf mulch, rotted logs, and in wet sand.

The Green Snakes

Opheodrys

People often mistakenly think these delicate, harmless little snakes are poisonous. The fact is, they are great consumers of insect larvae such as cutworms and are valuable to gardeners. A very slender, keeled-scaled species, *O. aestivus*, occurs in the Coastal Plain while a smaller, smoother one, *O. vernalis*, inhabits the North, east of the Rockies.

Rainbow Snake

Abastor erythrogrammus

Like the mud snake (p. 33), this brightly colored, shiny snake spends most of its time below ground in moist situations. It is rarely seen by humans. It lives in the eastern Coastal Plain and may attain 5 feet.

The Ring-necked Snakes

Diadophis punctatus

These clean-looking, glossy little snakes with neck ring and underside colors of yellow, orange, or red are easily identified. In shape and habits they resemble tiny king snakes but seldom grow to more than a foot long. Five varieties of this species occur east of the Rocky Mountains.

Prairie King Snake

Lampropeltis calligaster

Another of the large "family" of king snakes is this species, which is also called the yellow-bellied king snake. It seldom grows to more than 3 feet long. Older individuals are frequently uniform brown. Central, Prairie, and some Coastal Plain areas are its general range.

Common Hog-nosed Snake

Heterodon platyrhinos

Few of our harmless snakes are as stout in form as these reptiles and probably none practices such an astonishing bag of tricks to mislead its enemies. The turned-up rostral scale on the noses of these snakes helps them to root out the toads that form the bulk of their diet. They also have some enlarged teeth at the rear of their jaws to hold and perhaps to puncture this active prey. The eastern hog-nosed snake shown here is one of three species that range from the Atlantic coast to the Rockies and is the largest of the group, sometimes exceeding 3 feet in length. The western and southern hog-nosed snakes, *H. nasicus* and *H. simus*, though somewhat smaller, have even more developed, shovel-like noses. They are all egg-layers.

Because they live in rather open situations and are not exactly built for speed, hog-nosed snakes are probably often without a place to hide when their enemies appear. They meet such emergencies with two interesting tricks. First is the "bluff," in which the snake flattens its head and neck into a sinister shape, puffs itself up, and hisses and strikes in a threatening manner. (The mouth is kept closed during all this, and these snakes can rarely be induced to bite.) If this doesn't scare off the attacker, the snake appears to have convulsions, writhes and rolls and gapes its mouth and ends up lying still on its back. (If turned upright, the hog-nose quickly rolls upside down again!) It can be poked or pinched with no sign of life, but if after several minutes no harm comes to it, the snake takes a cautious peek around. One small motion will cause it to drop "dead" again, but if danger has passed, it rolls over and hurries off. Needless to say, the puffing and hissing frighten many people, who think the snake dangerous and call it a "puff adder" or a "blow viper."

Dekay's Snake and Red-bellied Snake

Storeria dekayi and *S. occipitomaculata*

There are a number of species of small snakes in the United States whose adult size is only about a foot long, and Dekay's snake is among the most common of these. It has managed to survive even in parks and vacant lots in the larger eastern cities, and quite frequently "nests" of several dozen hibernating specimens are unearthed during digging operations. Like the garter and water snakes, to which it is related, Dekay's snake is a live-bearing species, and its babies are surprisingly large at birth. A 10-inch female may deliver several young, each over 4 inches long!

The red-bellied snake is very similar to Dekay's, but it has darker dorsal color and is usually less abundant. Both of these snakes occur largely in the eastern half of the nation and both feed predominantly on slugs, snails, and earthworms.

Ribbon Snake

Thamnophis sauritus

"Ribbon snake" is a good descriptive name for these slender, delicate-looking reptiles. Here is an example showing that length is not necessarily an index of size in certain species of snakes. These snakes, averaging about 2 feet long, are barely thicker than a pencil, while hog-nosed snakes averaging the same length may be four times that diameter and weigh ten or fifteen times as much.

Fields and forest margins near water are favorite lurking places for ribbon snakes, for here they find the small frogs and salamanders that comprise their diet. This species is exceedingly quick and agile in catching its prey or eluding enemies in the tall grass. Three varieties occur, which together range from the Great Plains to the east coast.

The Garter Snakes

Thamnophis

Among the few kinds of snakes that people generally recognize as harmless are the garter snakes. They range from coast to coast across the United States, Canada, and Mexico. These reptiles often resemble the ribbon snakes in markings but are proportionately stouter and coarser, more like water snakes in shape. No less than twenty-nine forms of garter snakes are recognized, varying from the little striped Butler's garter snake of the Central Prairies, which averages less than 20 inches long, to the dun-colored giant garter snake of California, *T. gigas*, which may attain 5 feet in length. Between such extremes are the garter snakes shown here. The red-sided one is a far western form, while the other two are of the eastern group. The usual adult length is 20 to 30 inches.

When frightened or angry, garter snakes often flatten out in such a way as to look quite ferocious. Not only does the body appear thicker and the coloration between the scales stand out vividly, but the head takes on a wide-jawed, triangular appearance which is thought by some people to be the certain mark of a poisonous snake. Although rattlesnakes often flatten in this same fashion, so do water snakes, garter snakes, and other harmless species. Another feature of the garter snakes and their relatives, the water snakes, is the rather strong odor of the cloacal contents and musk from the anal scent glands, which they eject when caught or injured.

Garter snakes inhabit all sorts of terrain, but most of them have some liking for the vicinity of water. This is probably because when adult the majority feed on frogs, toads, or fish. They also eat considerable quantities of earthworms and insects. The young are born alive in litters which vary from 4 to 78 in number, according to the size and species of the female.

Queen Snake

Natrix septemvittata

Like other water snakes, queen snakes often climb up on bushes and branches overhanging a stream margin to sun themselves. If disturbed they drop into the stream with a splash and swim quickly underwater to shelter among aquatic plants or in holes in the bank. In such holes, in the streams usually inhabited by queen snakes, they are likely to find crayfish, which constitute the bulk of their diet. These rather small striped snakes are rarely over 2 feet long and rather slender. Queen snakes occur from the vicinity of Philadelphia, west to Wisconsin, and south to northern Florida.

The Plain-bellied Water Snakes

Natrix erythrogaster

Five distinct species of large water snakes occur in the United States. The largest of these is the big brown water snake, *N. taxispilota*, of the Southeast, which is said to grow to 6 feet. However, because some of the others, such as the plain-bellied water snakes and common water snakes, are more widely distributed, our space has been devoted to these forms.

The plain-bellied water snakes are so called because they have no markings on the underside, which is of a uniform yellow, red, or copper color. When young, their backs are cross-banded, but as they grow older they become nearly uniform brown. The one shown here is the red-bellied form, but three other subspecies are known. Together they range through the Coastal Plain, Central and Prairie regions. Maximum length is about 5 feet.

The Common Water Snakes

Natrix sipedon

Throughout the eastern half of the United States these snakes are among the most common species found along streams, rivers, and lakes. They are, like the truly aquatic reptiles, able to "hold their breath" for long periods under water and almost always take to the water when frightened or pursued.

Thirty to 40 inches is the usual length of the adults, but occasionally one over 4 feet long is seen. Stout of body and coarse-scaled, a large water snake is not reassuring in appearance and is often mistaken for the poisonous cottonmouth moccasin. In the South, where the cottonmouth occurs, there is some excuse for this, but in the northern states there are no poisonous water snakes (see page 19). Although species like the common and red-bellied water snakes are without venom or fangs, they do have teeth (like all snakes) and angry dispositions when restrained. Flattening the head and body into quite forbidding outlines, a cornered specimen will strike savagely and can make unpleasant, deep scratches on a bare hand. Some mild antiseptic is all the treatment needed.

The two snakes shown here are mature and half-grown examples of the northern variety, which has the broadest range of any of the common water snakes. About nine other subspecies of this snake occur, most of them in the southern states. The Mississippi water snakes, *N. s. confluens*, is one variety recognized by its few very wide crossbands and a dark gray and yellow coloration. Three forms of the common water snake have flattened tails and live along the Florida and Gulf coasts. They are called salt marsh water snakes.

All of these snakes feed on frogs, fish, salamanders, and other aquatic animals, and all bring forth their young alive in large numbers. A litter of 35 or 40 babies is quite common, and occasionally 75 or 80 young are born at a time.

Other Western Snakes

Here are some snakes typical of the southwestern and Pacific states. The glossy snakes, *Arizona*, have markings similar to the bull snakes but very pale in color, hence their other name of "faded" snake. Rarely over 3 feet long, these highly nocturnal snakes range from western Nebraska to California and down into Mexico.

The slender, striped patch-nosed snakes, *Salvadora*, are found in the west coast and Mexican border states and acquire their name from the squarish scale on the end of the nose. They are fast-moving, diurnal species, like racers, and average between 2 and 3 feet in length.

The banded sand snake, *Chilomeniscus*, which is only about 10 inches long, is a thickset, powerful burrower. It inhabits true sand deserts and uses its wedge-like head in pushing its way along beneath the surface, emerging only at night.

Among the snakes that live in the more moist, forested regions are the western ring-necked snakes, *Diadophis*, and the stout "rubber" boa, *Charina*. The ring-necks are much like the eastern species (p. 34) but show more red in their coloration and are considerably larger. The "rubber" boa is a shy, semi-burrowing snake that feeds largely on mice, which it constricts in true boa fashion. These stout snakes range from California to British Columbia and east into Montana and Wyoming. They average 18 to 24 inches long.

Before closing this section on snakes we should explain the loreal "pits" possessed by rattlesnakes, copperheads, and moccasins. These two small openings are located on each side of the snake's head, between eye and nostril, and are more noticeable than the nostrils. They serve as "radar" range finders and are so sensitive to heat and air currents that a snake can determine the location of a nearby warm-blooded creature without the aid of eyesight, and strike it with unerring accuracy.

Reptiles: Lizards

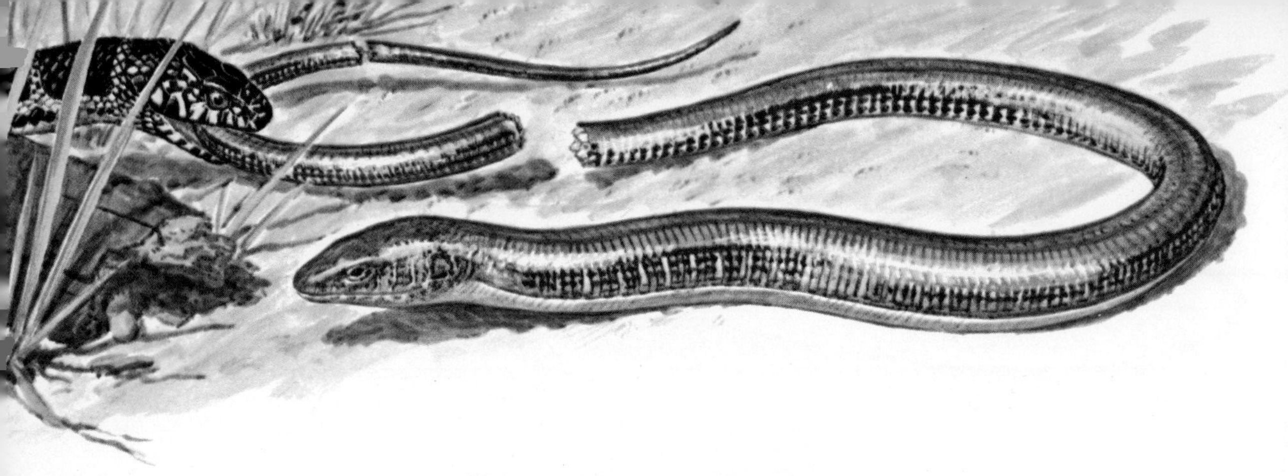

The Glass "Snakes"

Ophisaurus

These interesting reptiles, although legless, are classed as lizards. They have several features not possessed by any snake, such as eyelids and ear openings, and each polished scale is underlaid by a small piece of bone, giving a rather stiffly plated character to the body. Glass "snakes" have very long, very brittle tails which break off at the slightest blow or pull, hence their common name. Losing their tails is a trick of many lizards and it serves them well, for when seized by an enemy the tail not only breaks off but wriggles attractively while the lizard slips safely away. A new but shorter tail grows from the stump.

Glass "snakes" live in the Coastal Plain and some Prairie and Central areas and feed on insects, worms, snails, and smaller lizards. The female lays eggs and broods them until hatching. Average adult length is about 2 feet.

Six-lined Racerunner

The Racerunners

Cnemidophorus

Few reptiles are as fast afoot or as birdlike in motion as the well-named racerunners. Unlike most of our lizards, they often dig tunnels for shelter or for egg-laying purposes, and the speed with which they can dash into these holes must be seen to be believed. About sixteen forms occur, which range from coast

California Racerunner

to coast, largely in the southwestern states. While a few species have throat markings of bright orange or blue, most have rather subdued colors. All the racerunners have a granular scalation above, and large, squarish plates beneath. Adults may measure from 5 to 20 inches, according to species.

Five-lined Skink

Eumeces fasciatus

The five-lined skinks are typical of many American skinks in that they are brightly striped when hatched and gradually change with age until they are quite a different color. The young of this species, which is found from Massachusetts to the Great Plains, and Skilton's skink of the far western states have stripes and bright blue tails. In some species the young may have pink tails.

These lively, glossy lizards are abroad only in daylight hours and spend the nights and colder weather in rotted logs or burrows in the ground. There in late spring the female lays 6 to 12 eggs and coils around them, keeping guard until they are hatched. Ordinarily the food is insects, worms, and spiders. Adults are 5 to 8 inches long.

Mature male Greater Skink (E. laticeps)

Gila Monster: Beaded Lizard

Heloderma suspectum

There are only two kinds of lizards known to have a poisonous bite, and one of these, the beaded lizard, or Gila monster, occurs in the United States. It is strictly confined to the Great Desert region, largely in Arizona. The scales of the Gila are shaped like beads or minute cones, and each one contains a bony deposit. River beds and dry washes are among its favorite haunts, and it moves about largely at night. Captive Gilas eat eggs, the contents of which they lap up with their tongues. Their diet in a wild state includes lizards, mice, and carrion. Maximum length is about 24 inches.

Although usually slow-moving and deliberate, a beaded lizard can, when aroused, snap at offending objects with a sudden violence that may carry it almost off the ground. If it gets a good hold, its grip is powerful and it hangs on like a bulldog, allowing the venom in glands along the lower jaw to flow down the grooved teeth into the wound. The effects of this quite potent venom may differ considerably. There have been cases where the victims nearly died and others where there were little or no symptoms of poisoning.

The Alligator Lizards

Gerrhonotus

The heavy, keeled scalation probably accounts for the common name of these lizards. They appear to be closely related to the glass "snakes." Although comparatively slow-moving, their abilities in concealment, climbing, escape, and feeding make up for any lack of sprinting power. The ten varieties are confined to the western half of the country. The northern species, shown here, *G. coeruleus*, averages about 10 inches long, but the big Texas alligator lizards may attain 20 inches.

The Horned "Toads": Horned Lizards

Phrynosoma

These harmless but spiny reptiles are popularly called "horned toads" but they are actually true lizards, though of a most unusual form. There are at least six species and as many varieties occurring in the western United States, most particularly in the Desert, Basin, and Plateau areas. All of them prefer a dry, rather flat terrain in which to live. During the night or in rainy weather they usually burrow into the sand, but when the day is clear and warm they are alert and active in the bright, hot sun.

Sometimes horned "toads" are sold by thoughtless persons as souvenirs and as such they soon waste away and die. Captive specimens need a sizable wire cage, a thick layer of dry sand on its floor, plenty of sunlight, and some soft-bodied insects like moths or small caterpillars, ants, and especially spiders. The little water they drink must be supplied by dripping it in the cage daily, as they seem unable to drink from a bowl. Although some species of horned lizards bear live young and others lay eggs, they are reputed to have one surprising trick in common. This is the ability, when restrained and frightened (or angry), to spurt a thin jet of blood from a corner of the eye. The purpose of this is not known, but it is none the less astonishing.

Of the species shown below, the short-horned lizards are the smallest, averaging about 4 inches long. The regal horned lizard may reach 7 inches, and the other two are of intermediate size.

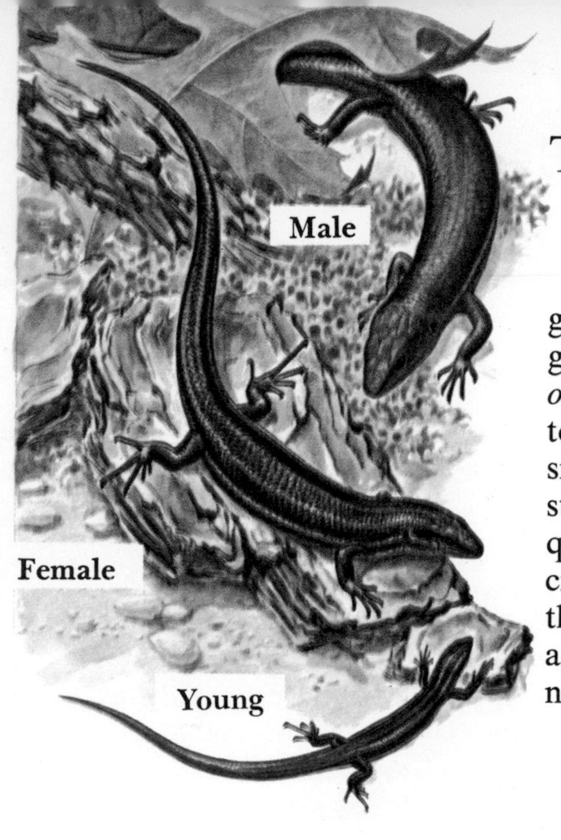

The Large Skinks: "Scorpions"

Eumeces laticeps and *E. obsoletus*

Skinks are a numerous and successful group of lizards of mostly small size, but our greater skink, *laticeps*, and the Sonoran skink, *obsoletus*, grow to be a foot long. Their scales, too, are hard and glossy, each one enclosing a small bone. With this supple armor, their strong jaws and active habit, the skinks are quite formidable for their size. The larger species will even tackle wasps and young mice, and the greater skink of our Southeast is also an agile climber. Its western relative, the big Sonoran skink, is more terrestrial in habit.

Red Scaly Lizard

Sceloporus poinsetti

Several of the fence lizard clan grow to about a foot long and have exceptionally bristly scales. They are known as scaly lizards or giant swifts and occur chiefly in the southwestern states. The red scaly lizard, characterized by a black collar going completely across the neck and a reddish color, lives in west Texas, southern New Mexico, and Mexico. Unlike some of its relatives, it rarely goes into trees but inhabits dry, rocky situations. A particularly fine-looking species, the granite scaly lizard, *Sceloporus orcutti*, lives in southern California. It is a bronze or coppery tone with a clear blue spot in the middle of each scale.

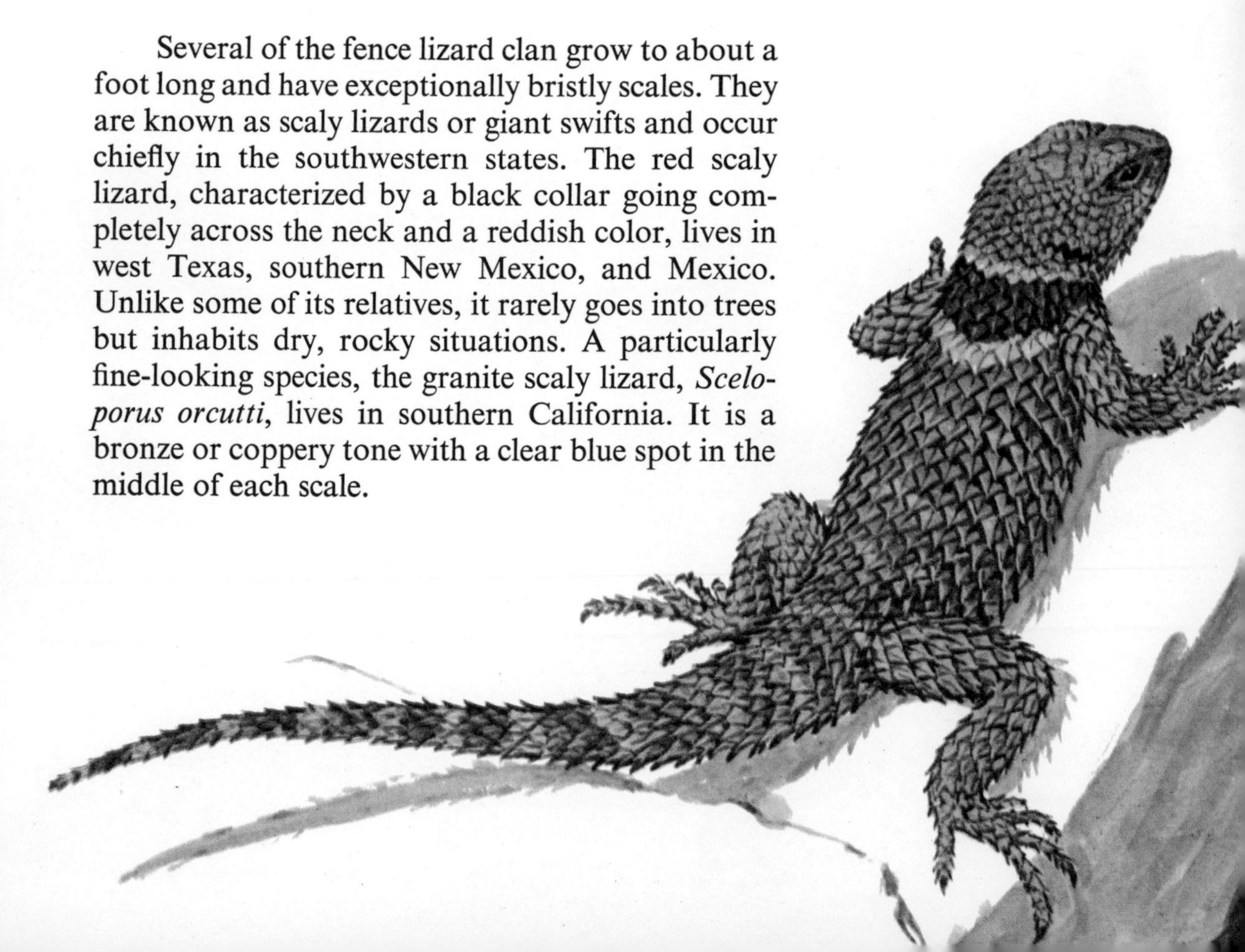

Chuckwalla

Sauromalus obesus

With the exception of the Gila monster, the chuckwalla is our largest lizard. It occurs only in the great Desert region of the Southwest and is unlike most North American lizards in two respects: its vegetarian diet of plants, blossoms, and fruits (remarkable in an area where the vegetation is sparse and tough) and its means of resisting capture. Chuckwallas inhabit rocky areas and when frightened they take refuge in cracks between boulders, as many other lizards do. But as the enemy, be it man or beast, tries to extract the chuckwalla from this position the lizard so inflates its lungs with air that it is stuck fast and can be gotten out only with great difficulty, if at all!

This is an egg-laying species, but little else is known of its breeding habits. Young chuckwallas are brighter colored than the adults and have pronounced crossband markings that become blurred and darkened with age. Adults average about 15 inches long.

Anole: "Chameleon"

Anolis carolinensis

Each year thousands of these lizards are sold as "chameleons" at circuses and usually die from lack of proper care. Actually they are American lizards called anoles and are not related to the true chameleons of the Old World. They do, however, have the ability to change color (possessed by many lizards to a degree) and can turn from brown to vivid green in a matter of seconds. This is not a conscious effort on the lizard's part to match its background but rather the result of excitement, light, or temperature changes. Anoles are also great acrobats, and with the assistance of the little suction "ribs" on the undersides of their toes they can climb a smooth wall with ease. The males have a means of dilating their throats in display, which fans out the skin to show bright red between the scales.

These lizards occur in the southeastern quarter of the nation and if kept as pets need warmth and sun to thrive. Live, soft-bodied insects and spiders are suitable food. Water must be sprinkled into the cage daily for them to drink. Maximum length is about 8 inches.

Fence Lizard: Pine Swift

Sceloporus undulatus

The fence lizard group is distributed over the whole southern two thirds of the United States, ranging as far north as Washington on the west coast and up to southern New Jersey in the East. The ones shown here are from the Coastal Plain pinewoods.

A prickly scalation and rather snug, compact build are characteristic of these lizards. They are quick and alert and when pursued show great agility, running and dodging about tree trunks and fence rails on which they so often bask. The adult males at mating time display the vivid blue areas on the underside of their bodies and necks. The young, which are hatched from eggs, are colored more like the females.

Some Western Lizards

Ground Gecko

Night Lizard

By far the greatest number and variety of our lizards occur in the arid southwestern states. One of these is the delicate-looking ground gecko. *Coleonyx*, which prowls at night and has the vertical slit pupils so typical of the eyes of a nocturnal animal. The scalation of these lizards is so fine and soft as to be almost salamander-like in appearance. Length is about 5 inches. The geckos are among the few reptiles that can make a vocal sound, usually a squeaking noise which in some species is said to sound like "Gecko, Gecko."

The night lizards, *Xantusia*, have secretive habits somewhat similar to the ground geckos. Their eyes lack movable lids and so are always "open" like those of a snake. The desert night lizard shown here, *X. vigilis*, has a rather uniform color with a speckling of black dots and seldom measures

over 4 inches long. Another species, the island night lizard, *X. riversiana*, is a larger, thickset form attaining about 8 inches. It occurs on the Santa Barbara Islands. Both these lizards bear their young alive.

Seldom are an animal's scientific and common names alike, but such is the case with the ground utas, *Uta*. The spotted one shown here is a common ground uta, *U. stansburiana*. These are small diurnal lizards which occur from Texas to California and up to Washington. They resemble the smaller swifts, *Sceloporus*, in form and colors but do not have bristly scalation. Like some other lizards, they may dig burrows in which they take refuge from extreme temperatures or enemies.

Like certain other desert lizards, the gridiron-tailed lizard, *Callisaurus*, displays black and white bars under the tail, in strong contrast to the sand colors of the rest of the tail and body. The amazing speed with which these lizards run, the flashily marked tail curled upward to display its striped underside, followed by sudden stops with tail lowered, serves to confuse the vision of any pursuer. Average length is about 7 inches.

Reptiles: Turtles, Tortoises, and Terrapins

The Soft-shelled Turtles

Trionyx

Unlike most turtles, these reptiles are flexible, rubbery creatures, so flat and so nearly circular that they are sometimes called "flapjacks." Their limbs are extensively webbed for swimming in the streams and rivers they inhabit, and they are so muscular and quick they can literally run on land. The head, with its "snorkel" snout, has razor-sharp jaws covered by soft lips. A large captive specimen (some attain a shell length of 18 inches) can be nasty and dangerous, for it will snap like a striking snake.

Soft-shelled turtles occur from the west slope of the Appalachian area and the southern Coastal Plain to the Rockies and to southern California. A bottom view of the baby southern soft-shell is shown at left.

Chicken Turtle

Deirochelys reticularia

Two outstanding things about these turtles are their very long, narrow heads and necks and the broad yellow stripe covering the lower half of their front legs. Another characteristic is the zebra-like striping of the "hip" area. The species occurs in the extreme lower or southern parts of the Coastal Plain.

In general appearance chicken turtles resemble the terrapins, but the rather rough shell is proportionately narrower and deeper and, in spite of the fact that they are water dwellers, they travel about on land quite often. Food consists largely of small water creatures. Average shell length is about 7 inches.

The Gopher Tortoises

Gopherus

These are our only true tortoises. They are found along the southern edge of the country, one species in the California-Arizona deserts, one in Texas, and one (shown here) in the sandy portions of the southeastern states. While they are all good burrowers, the eastern form is an especially good engineer and digs tunnels which may be 20 or more feet long and yards deep in which it takes refuge from heat, cold, rain, and enemies. Many other animals use the holes made by these good-natured, elephant-footed, and heavily armored vegetarians. Maximum length is about 14 inches.

Red-eared Terrapin

Pseudemys scripta elegans

Here is just one of many turtles called terrapins or "sliders" that inhabit freshwater ponds and rivers in the United States. This form, with two scarlet head stripes, occurs in the great Mississippi Basin area, but other related varieties are found in the Coastal Plain to the east and west.

Baby red-eared terrapins are often sold in pet stores. These brightly colored youngsters become darker with maturity, and old male specimens may be almost totally black. Their food is similar to the southern terrapins (p. 54) and includes water plants, fish, insects, and the like. Maximum shell length is about 9 inches.

The Southern Terrapins: "Sliders" or "Cooters"

Pseudemys floridana

The name "southern terrapin" is used here to include about eight varieties of turtles which range over the southern United States from Maryland and southern Illinois to Mexico. Like the subspecies of the red-eared terrapin group, each of these forms has certain differences of color, shell shape, or size. Although most adults average 9 to 12 inches long, one form that occurs in Florida, *P. f. suwanniensis*, may attain a shell length of 16 inches. Unlike most fresh-water turtles, it sometimes ventures downstream into salt-water bays.

Throughout most of the year these turtles forage streams and lakes for the small water creatures and aquatic vegetation they feed upon, or sun themselves in colonies on fallen trees and stream banks. Irregularly they venture on land in traveling from one watercourse to another, but at least one yearly pilgrimage is made ashore by the females to lay their eggs. The first thing the female must do is find a suitable nesting site, which is usually on a sun-drenched sand bank. Here she digs with her hind feet in a remarkably deft manner until she has fashioned a roughly vase-shaped hole several inches deep in which she lays her eggs. These are about 1½ inches long and from 10 to 30 in number. The female then covers the hole with soil and leaves the eggs to incubate in the warmth of the sun. They usually hatch in three to four months' time, when the babies dig their way out and head for the water. This pattern of reproduction is typical of turtles in general. The adult male terrapins, which can be recognized by their immensely long front claws, have no part in the reproductive cycle beyond the mating season.

The Painted Turtles

Chrysemys picta

These are the most abundant water turtles in the northern half of the United States, and nearly every pond, lake, or roadside pool contains its share of painted turtles. They are very fond of sun bathing, and whenever the weather is warm enough as many as twenty or thirty may be seen on a single floating log. Shy of human beings and keen of vision, they tumble into the water at the first hint of danger to hide among the weeds and debris of the pond bottom, but when captured an adult painted turtle usually struggles energetically to escape and may even snap at fingers that come near its head.

The name "painted turtle" comes, of course, from the especially vivid color markings, which are most pronounced in the young. Four varieties (subspecies) may be recognized. The eastern painted, shown above, is found east of the Appalachian Mountains, the Central form inland to the Prairies, and the western race continues the range on out to the Cascade region of Washington. The southern one, with a noticeable light stripe down the back, is a Mississippi Valley form. It is the smallest of the four, averaging about 5 inches long. The Western is the largest, often reaching 8 or 9 inches, while the other varieties are between these extremes in size. Males are smaller and flatter than the females and have long front claws. During the courting period they wiggle them in the female's face in an odd manner. In the late spring the females go ashore to lay their eggs in typical turtle fashion. These are 4 to 15 in number and of a pinkish color.

Food of these turtles includes aquatic insects and plants, water lily seeds, carrion, and occasionally small frogs or fish.

Western

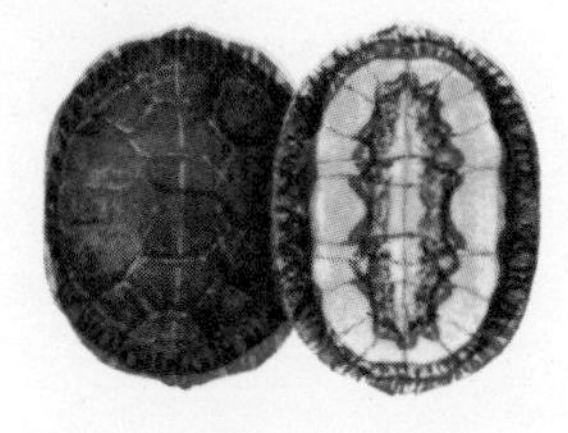
Central

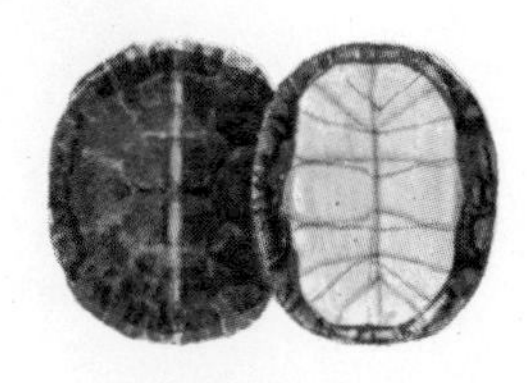
Southern

The Sawback Turtles

Graptemys pseudogeographica

Sawback turtles have a pointed keel on each of the central shields of their top shells which give the back a "sawtooth" outline when viewed from the side. These keels are rather low and rounded in old turtles, but in the brightly colored babies, like the Mississippi sawback shown here, they are very pronounced. The attractive infant turtles are often seen in pet shops with the young of other species and usually do well in captivity if they receive proper food, sunlight (*without* overheating), and clean water in their tank.

The sawbacks are midwestern turtles and occur in waters of the Prairie region and in the Mississippi and Gulf drainages of the Coastal Plain.

Map Turtle

Graptemys geographica

Few turtles are as hard to catch or as delicate in captivity as the map turtle. It lives mostly in large streams and rivers and has an unusual range for a water turtle. This extends from Vermont and parts of Virginia west through the Central region to Minnesota and Kansas and about halfway down the Mississippi Valley. The name "map turtle" comes from the network of yellow lines on its upper shell. Another mark of identification is the round or triangular yellow spot back of each eye.

A strong central keel is noticeable on the backs of young map turtles, and this species shares several other traits with the sawback and the diamond back terrapins. One is the tendency for old females to develop very large heads and jaws (shown here), and another is the diet, which is largely snails and crawfish.

The Box Turtles

Terrepene

These are our most abundant land turtles, and even city people out for weekend picnics have usually encountered one at some time or another. Five varieties occur east of the Rocky Mountains, only one of which has extended its range farther west, but because they are all so much alike we shall use the common box turtle, *T. carolina*, as a general example.

Firstly, the name "box" refers to the reptile's ability to close the upper and lower halves of its shell by means of a "hinge" across the lower side, or plastron, when frightened. Sometimes a very young or very stout specimen can only partly close (like the mud turtles, p. 60), but usually this structure well protects the more tender parts, and enemies like fox and lynx would be unable to damage seriously a closed-up box turtle. However, speeding automobiles and brush fires spell death to thousands of specimens each year. This seems too bad, because these turtles are quite harmless and feed on earthworms, toadstools, wild berries, slugs, snails, and carrion.

Although they are essentially land animals, some of them enter shallow water frequently, and in very hot weather they may burrow into mucky ground and remain there for weeks to keep cool. The eggs are usually laid in June and the babies, hatching in late summer, are very secretive and seldom seen by people. Adult males usually have bright red eyes and longer, heavier limbs than the females and concave lower shells.

The Diamondback Terrapins

Malaclemys terrapin

Most aquatic turtles live in fresh water or in the open sea, but diamondback terrapins are denizens of the salt marshes and similar shore areas. About six varieties are known to occur along different parts of the Atlantic and Gulf coasts. All have rather subdued colors of pale gray and rusty brown with black and tan markings. The bumpy keel up the back is quite pronounced in adults.

Females are much larger than males, with greatest length for each being 9 and 6 inches, respectively. The one shown here is a baby. Hatchlings like this were once raised in pens until grown and then sold as a great food delicacy.

Wood Turtle

Clemmys insculpta

Few reptiles seem as intelligent as these handsome turtles with their "carved-looking" shells and alert dark eyes. The adults, which are 6 to 9 inches long, have a rich red color under the legs and neck, and their lower shells are yellow with black blotches. Altogether, the wood turtles are most interesting, for in addition to their subtle coloring and gentle manners they are well equipped for both land and water travel and eat a great variety of foods, snails and berries being especially favored. They appear to live most successfully in bunch-grass meadows where cool streams flow.

This turtle occurs in the upper northeastern quarter of the United States and in southeastern Canada.

Musk Turtles: "Stinkin' Jim"

Sternotherus

Fishermen and country people may be familiar with these little turtles which often take a baited hook and when landed exude a strong odor in their fright which has earned them the names of "stinkin' Jim" or "stinkpot." Mud turtles also have scent glands.

Musk turtles are specifically water dwellers but forage by crawling about stream bottoms rather than by swimming. The common musk turtle, shown here, which occurs over the eastern half of the country, seldom comes out on land except to lay its eggs, but the southern musk turtles, *S. carinatus*, are reported to be great sun bathers. Both of these species are much inclined to bite when captured. Their big pointed heads equip them well for such defense. Their shells are seldom more than 4 inches long, but the tiny hatchlings are no bigger than a large bean. These reptiles are valuable water scavengers.

Pacific Pond Turtle

Clemmys marmorata

Although huge sea turtles occasionally visit the west coast, California, Washington, and Oregon have altogether only five species of native turtles. The Pacific pond turtle is found in all three states and is the common turtle there. Somewhat larger than the eastern spotted turtle (adults measure 5 to 7 inches), it is much like it in appearance and habits but seems to frequent all sorts of wet situations, including salt marshes.

Spotted Turtle

Clemmys guttata

These attractive, rather gentle relatives of the wood turtle are found largely in the extreme eastern and north-central areas. Among the easiest of turtles to identify, their black or dark brown shells with yellow dots distinguish them from the gaudy painted turtles with whom they frequently share a sunny pond shore or floating log. Most commonly, spotted turtles are seen in woodland streams or open bogs, but sometimes they turn up in brackish water margins and often make long journeys on land.

In the spring they are among the earliest reptiles to appear, and occasionally courting males may be observed chasing their prospective mates over grass and through puddles with great vigor and persistence. Strangely, the young are very seldom seen and little is known of their habits. Food consists largely of insects and minute water creatures, but some plants and carrion may also be eaten.

The Mud Turtles

Kinosternon

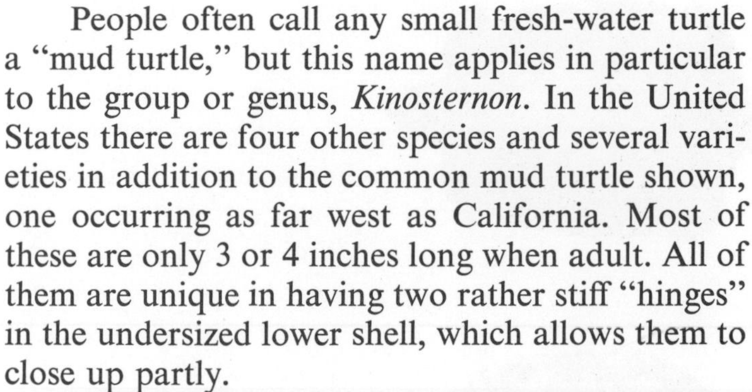

People often call any small fresh-water turtle a "mud turtle," but this name applies in particular to the group or genus, *Kinosternon*. In the United States there are four other species and several varieties in addition to the common mud turtle shown, one occurring as far west as California. Most of these are only 3 or 4 inches long when adult. All of them are unique in having two rather stiff "hinges" in the undersized lower shell, which allows them to close up partly.

Mud turtles inhabit many sorts of situations from shallow lakes to ditches and bogs, yet often prowl on land. Their food includes worms, fruit, carrion, and insects and they may be active day or night.

Common Snapping Turtle

Chelydra serpentina

Few American reptiles are as large and sinister-looking as the snapping turtle. The common snapper occurs from the Rocky Mountains to the Atlantic coast and, like the alligator snapper (p 62), it has a small, cross-shaped lower shell, a large head, and long tail. However, its neck is proportionately longer and it is a more active turtle. The general appearance, particularly of a specimen walking on land, is that of a thickset, powerful creature. In addition to its walking, swimming, and bottom-crawling activities, the common snapper can strike with the speed of a snake and can inflict a savage bite. Large snappers can be dangerous on land but when submerged are more inclined to hide or seek deep water if alarmed. Fifteen inches is recorded as the greatest length attained by the common snapper, but 18 inches is probably nearer the actual maximum. In any case, the shell length is deceiving, for an average-sized one with a 10-inch shell will measure 2 feet with neck and tail outstretched and may weigh 20 pounds or more. The top weight is over 60 pounds.

These turtles eat carrion, fish, frogs, snails, plants, water fowl—in fact, anything they can seize in their hooked jaws. The rough-shelled baby snappers feed as voraciously as their parents and are not too safe to keep in aquariums with other small turtles or fish. They are hatched from spherical eggs laid by the female turtles in a sand bank or plowed field in early summer. Twenty to 30 eggs is the usual number in a clutch.

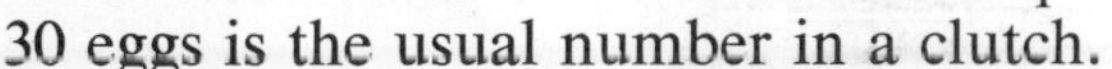

Giant Turtles

The alligator snapping turtle, *Macrochelys*, grows larger than any of our fresh-water turtles, often weighing over 150 pounds. It seems to be less ferocious than the common snapper in spite of its huge armor-plated head and heavy, hooked jaws. This turtle lives in the Mississippi and Gulf river drainages and is most active at night. It captures much of its food by lying quietly on the stream bottom with mouth agape, waiting for some unwary creature to nibble at the moving, wormlike bit of flesh that grows from the turtle's tongue. When this happens, the terrible jaws snap shut with lightning speed and crushing power.

In warmer parts of the Atlantic and Pacific coasts huge sea turtles may be encountered when they come ashore to lay their eggs or when they get entangled in fishermen's nets. These reptiles are equipped for marine living and have limbs like great flippers, but they are essentially air-breathers. The green turtle, *Chelonia*, is used for food, while another smaller species, the hawksbill, *Eretmochelys*, has a shell covering that is used to make "tortoise-shell" combs. The loggerhead turtle, *Caretta*, and the "Ridley," *Lepidochelys*, are two others.

The Leatherback or trunk turtle, *Dermochelys coriacea*, is the largest of living turtles, and one weighing nearly a ton was reported in 1907. The shell of this species is a smooth, leathery "hide" overlying bony plates and ridges, and the fins are so developed that there is even a web between hind flippers and tail.

Green Turtle

Hawksbill

Leatherback

Reptiles: Alligators

American Alligator

Alligator mississipiensis

The alligators, crocodiles, and their allies are giant reptiles that seem like holdovers from the age of dinosaurs. Massive and heavy-scaled, they are essentially creatures of tropical coasts and swamps, but a few, such as our American alligator, occur in temperate regions. In earlier days alligators were abundant throughout the lower Mississippi Valley and the Coastal Plain and attained lengths of over 18 feet; but now, through persistent killing, they have become quite scarce in most areas and the discovery of a 10-footer makes headlines.

"Bull" alligators bellow mightily in the swamps at breeding time and send forth a musky odor from glands under the jaw, thereby attracting the attention of the females. The female alligator deposits several dozen eggs in a "nesting mound" which she makes of leaves, twigs, and earth, and lets the heat of the sun and the rotting vegetation incubate them. The female guards the nest, and when the babies start hatching, the mother 'gator is said to dig them out when she hears the barking cries of the little ones. The lively 9-inch young (shown below on the nest) are full of spunk and evince a snappy interest in anything that moves and can be eaten. They grow quite rapidly with high temperatures, sun, and plenty of food, and a five-year-old 'gator may measure over 5 feet long.

Amphibians: Frogs

Bullfrog and Green Frog

Rana catesbeiana and *R. clamitans*

Because these two frogs are the first amphibians in this book, an outline life history of one, the bullfrog, is described below. It is quite typical of frogs and of amphibians in general. Bullfrogs usually live in larger bodies of fresh water like lakes and ponds, and as the breeding season begins in early summer the males start voicing their deep bass calls that sound like "jug-o-rum" or "better-go-'round." During mating, a female bullfrog deposits a mass of small beadlike eggs in the water, sometimes as many as 20,000, each one of which is surrounded by a sphere of jelly. These eggs develop into tiny larvae called "polliwogs" or "tadpoles" which escape from their jelly envelope and swim about, feeding on pond plants (algae) and carrion. At first they are a scant quarter inch long and have feathery external gills for "breathing," but later they become round-bodied and have internal gills somewhat like fishes. They remain in this stage for about two years, but toward the end of this time budding hind legs appear and front legs and lungs develop inside. When these organs have grown to a useful size the polliwogs (now 6 inches or so long) seek the surface for air, their tails shrink, and front legs poke through. In a few days they have become young frogs. Growth continues as they feed voraciously on insects, and in another two or three summers they may measure as much as 8 inches long with legs folded. They are our largest frogs, and big ones sometimes eat smaller frogs, baby snakes, or mice!

The smaller green frog has about the same life cycle but often inhabits woodland streams and starts "singing" earlier. Their call, sounding like a plucked banjo string, is "plung!" They may be distinguished from young bullfrogs by a dark-edged skin fold along each side of the body. Their natural range, like the bullfrog's, is east of the Rocky Mountains.

Wood Frog

Rana sylvatica

These frogs come to breed in woodland pools very early in the spring, sometimes before all the ice is melted. At this time their dark colors are quite different from the beautiful pale hues they show later on, and the males are very vocal. Their clucking calls sound much like the "talking" quack of ducks, and soon the females arrive and begin depositing their baseball-sized egg masses in the water. Within ten days or so all the adult wood frogs have usually left the ponds to spend the rest of the year in the forest. This is a frog of the Appalachian, Piedmont, and Central regions.

The Leopard Frogs

Rana pipiens

The leopard frogs occur over most of the country, and the half-dozen different forms display a remarkable variety in size, color, and markings. They inhabit many types of terrain, from desert water holes to coastal swamps, but are absent from the Pacific states except extreme eastern Washington and Oregon.

All of these frogs have a narrow, prominent ridge of skin from the eye down along each side, and their spots are usually rounder and smaller than those of the pickerel frog. The male leopards show a very evident pair of vocal sacs when they are "calling" (see lower picture). During early spring rains leopard frogs may migrate in large numbers from meadow or swamp to ponds or water holes, where they breed, and if there is a much-traveled road in their path large numbers of these handsome and valuable frogs are killed by automobiles.

Pickerel Frog

Rana palustris

Wet meadows, rocky brooks, and pond margins are typical places favored by these frogs. Like the leopard frogs, they are very active and great jumpers and seem to be equally at home on grassy land or in the water. The pickerel frog, essentially an eastern species of the Appalachian, Piedmont, and Central areas, differs from other spotted frogs of this region in the squarish form of its markings and the yellow-orange "flash marks" under its hind legs.

In spring, about the time the American toads are at the ponds, these frogs also have their breeding period; and the males, giving voice to their rather subdued, groaning calls, sound very strange indeed.

Red-legged Frog

Rana aurora

Perhaps one should call this the Pacific Coast wood frog, for in many ways it suggests the eastern form. At least three varieties occur, of which one, in a drier habitat in California, has quite a rough skin and more subdued colors. The red-legged frog may attain a fair size, 4 inches or so from snout to "rump," but it is the three-quarter-grown examples from the North which (as shown here) have the more vivid colors and pronounced pink-red under the belly and legs.

Yellow-legged Frog

Rana boyli

This, too, is a western frog, restricted to California and Oregon. It is usually a denizen of rocky streams and averages smaller than the red-legged species.

Cricket Frogs and Swamp Tree Frogs

Acris and *Pseudacris*

The "songs" of these frogs resemble cricket calls and have a crackling, metallic quality easily recognized if once heard. The frogs themselves are very small, usually less than an inch long, and occur largely east of the Rockies. Five forms of the cricket frogs, *Acris*, and eleven of the swamp tree frogs, *Pseudacris*, are recognized.

Gray Tree Frog

Hyla versicolor

"Tree toad" is also a common name for this frog, which occurs throughout most of the United States east of the Great Plains. Its color may vary from hour to hour, and it is often hard to detect one against a background of bark or leaf. Like all *Hylas*, it has suction pads on its toes and is an expert climber and gymnast. In spring, when the spatterdock leaves first appear, gray tree frogs come to the ponds to breed and their trilling calls ring through the mild evenings. In summer, too, often before a thunderstorm, they may call from treetops, where they feed on insects or sleep in some quiet shady nook.

Green Tree Frog

Hyla cinerea

The slender, attractive green tree frog with the bright stripe down its sides is essentially a southern marsh dweller and occurs throughout the Coastal Plain. Calls of these *Hylas* in chorus have been likened to the sound of many cowbells.

Spring Peeper

Hyla crucifer

This is the smallest of all our tree frogs, and its "peeping" voice is a familiar sound of spring throughout the eastern half of the United States. However, few people have seen these frogs. Tiny and delicate, these penny-sized tree frogs spend the warmer months of the year roaming the forest floor in search of insect food and the winters tucked snugly into some crevice beneath log or boulder. They come to the water early to breed, about the time the wood frogs appear (in March in the North), and leave again before hot weather arrives. Their best distinguishing feature is a roughly shaped x mark on the back.

Pacific Tree Frog

Hyla regilla

Most frogs change color from hour to hour and have variable markings, but this species of the Pacific coastal states shows greater variety and changes than most. It is a small frog, about 1½ inches long, and its call, recordings of which are often used in movies for "background" in outdoor scenes, is well known.

Amphibians: Toads

American Toad

Bufo terrestris americanus

Toads are different from frogs in many ways, particularly in their more compact form, shorter legs, very warty skin, and their land-dwelling habits. Some live in real desert locations but come out of moist hiding places only during the night or in rainy or cool weather. Like the frogs, toads feed largely on insects, but they have such enormous appetites that they were once estimated to be worth $20 each a year to farmers because they ate so many crop-destroying insects.

Like most amphibians, toads breed in the water, usually in ponds, meadows, or flooded ditches. The American toads, which inhabit the eastern and central states, usually come to the water in April. Then the clear, high-pitched "singing" of the males may be heard as their throats fill out like small balloons and vibrate with the sustained effort of their call. In this species it is a strangely sweet, trilling sound.

The eggs are laid in long strings of jelly, and after the tiny tadpoles (larvae) hatch they grow rapidly. Within two months or so they have developed legs, the tail begins shrinking, and they stay in very shallow water to get air for their newly acquired lungs. The babies often emerge on land in great numbers, and though many are eaten by enemies, enough survive to grow up. We should mention here that although an injured toad will exude a distasteful, slightly toxic milky fluid from its warts, it has no power to produce warts. About two dozen "kinds" of toads occur in the United States, but this common form is presented as typical of many in the group.

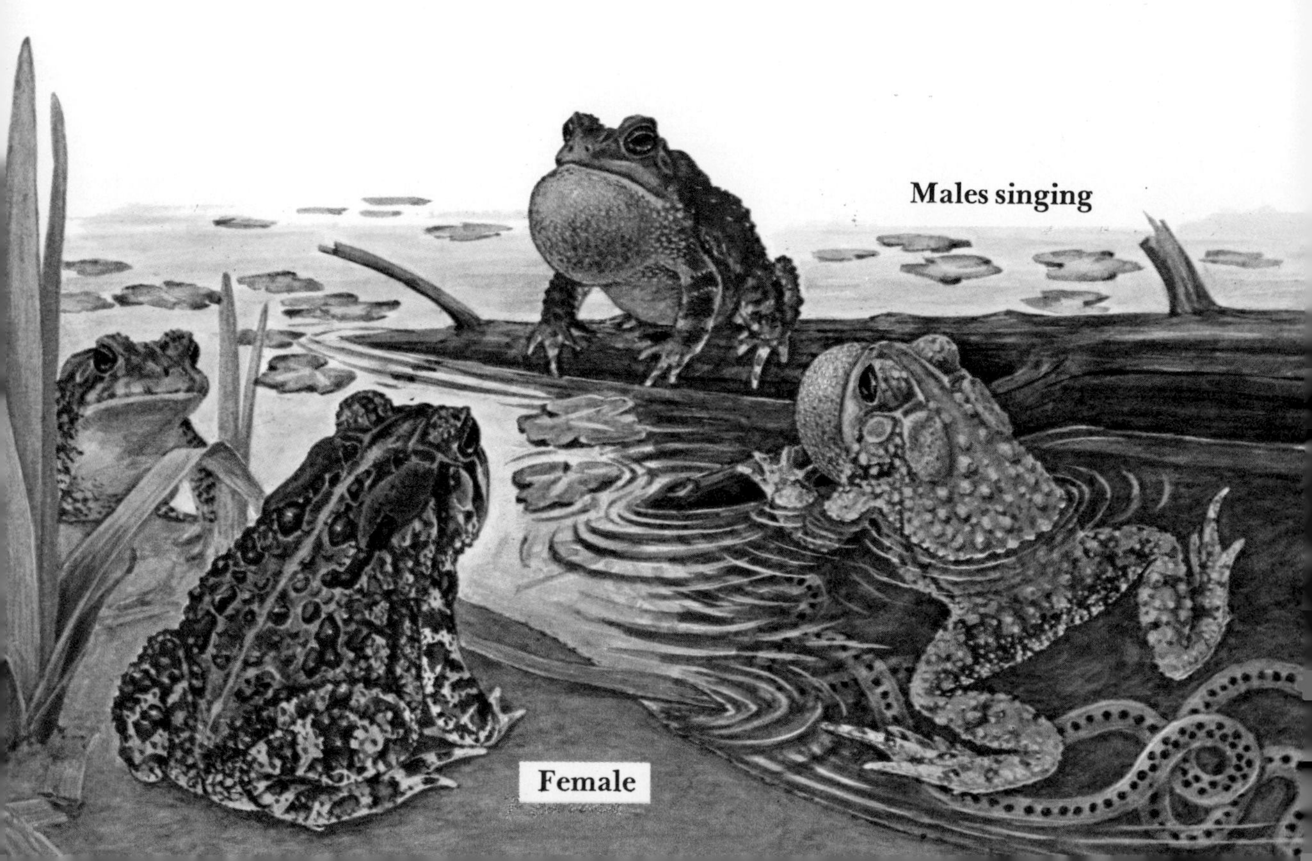

Narrow-mouthed Toad

Microhyla carolinensis

These interesting, odd little fellows may be recognized by a characteristic fold of skin around the neck just back of their eyes. However, one is more likely to hear their buzzing, insect-like calls than to see them, for the narrow-mouths are quick and very shy. They often hide in burrows beneath old boards or stones, but during warm rains may come to pools and puddles to breed.

These amphibians occur largely in the Coastal Plain, southern Prairie, and Great Plains areas.

Western

Eastern

The Spadefoot Toads

Scaphiopus

The spadefoots are great burrowers and spend much of their lives below ground. They have larger digging "spurs" than most toads and very prominent eyes with vertical, catlike pupils that give them a rather strange, surprised expression. The only time you are likely to see spadefoots is during very heavy, warm rains, when they come to ponds or flooded hollows to breed. A group of them will set up a tremendous clangor with their barking or droning calls, but they usually stay only a few hours and are gone the next day, leaving hundreds of egg "ropes" in the water. After hatching, the tadpoles may transform into baby toads in as few as 15 days.

Great Plains Toad

Bufo cognatus

This toad, just one of many western species, is also called the "sandhill toad." It occurs in some Desert and Basin areas in California, around the southern Rockies, and through the Great Plains. An interesting feature of the males is the throat pouch, which, when inflated in singing, is kidney-shaped and projects beyond the face. *Bufo cognatus* can withstand quite dry weather and has a prodigious appetite for grasshoppers and other insects.

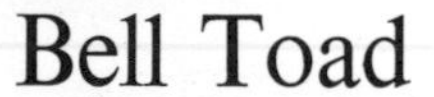

Bell Toad

Ascaphus truei

Before leaving the frog-toad group some mention should be made of the bell toad or tailed frog of our northwestern states. This seldom-seen amphibian has special features, such as primitive bony structures, an absence of external eardrums, and (in the male) a tail throughout life! It will serve to introduce the following section, although it is not actually related to the salamanders.

Amphibians: Terrestrial Salamanders

Long-tailed Salamander

Eurycea longicauda

In spite of their lizard-like shape, the salamanders are classified as amphibians. Froglike, they have moist, delicate skins, a fondness for damp places, and usually their young are water-dwelling larvae with gills. In fact, the most noticeable ways in which salamanders differ from frogs is in their long tails and bodies, short legs, and their liking for dark, secluded places during the day.

The long-tailed salamander shown here is proportionately one of our longest and narrowest salamanders and appears to live mostly among rocks at the edges of streams and at the mouths of caves. Several races of this species occur in a broad Appalachian and Coastal Plain area from New York to Louisiana.

The Western Newts

Taricha

Newt is a name applied to certain salamanders. Several species of these rather rough-skinned western newts occur from California to Alaska and, although most of them are land dwellers, all enter the water at breeding time. In addition to the more common type shown, one species, *T. rivularis*, is bright red beneath while another, from the San Diego region, has numerous warts, even on its toes.

Yellow-spotted Salamander

Ensatina escholtzi croceater

Among the many salamanders of our Far West, perhaps none is so spectacular-looking as this particular variety which occurs in California in the San Bernardino and nearby mountain ranges. It seems to be a land-dwelling form and, like most salamanders, it stays under cover during the day but may prowl at night and during damp weather. Adults measure about 5 inches.

Red-backed Salamander

Plethodon cinereus

The red-backs and lead-backs are two color phases of the same species. Occurring in the eastern United States and Canada to Hudson Bay, they are often the most common salamander in an area and may be turned up when rocks and logs are moved from damp places. Tiny and delicately made, they too are among the lungless (plethodontid) salamanders.

Red Salamander

Pseudotriton ruber

The young adults of this 4- to 6-inch salamander are most vividly colored, but with age they darken to more somber hues. The red salamander is generally a denizen of clear streams, springs, and bogs (though I have found them in rotted logs), and it occurs in about the same range as the long-tail. Like the red-backed salamander on this page, it is of the lungless type and "breathes" largely through its skin!

Eastern Newt: Red Eft

Diemictylus viridescens

These are the salamanders children often catch in the spring and call "lizards." Like the western newts, they possess true lungs and breed in water, but they have a different life history. After the eggs are laid and the tiny, gilled larvae have grown to an inch or two long, they absorb their gills and take up a land existence. During this period (one to three years) they are red in color and are called efts. Finally they return to the water to stay, grow tail fins, and assume the adult colors. In some areas of their range, which covers the whole eastern United States, these newts may skip the land stage altogether and may even retain short gills.

Jefferson's and Tiger Salamanders

Ambystoma

These are but two members of a large group. Jefferson's salamander is quite a slender form, very active in habits and usually found under logs near streams. Although speckled with whitish flecks when young, a mature specimen of 5 or 6 inches is almost uniform brown.

The tiger salamanders are widely distributed across the country and have great variety in color markings. With their near relatives, the spotted salamanders, *A. maculatum*, they are among the largest common land-dwelling species, although usually out of sight in some burrow or tunnel below the surface. They come to the ponds, often for just one night in the early spring, to breed and to lay their egg masses, which are each enclosed in a snug, thick outer envelope of jelly. After the larvae have hatched they grow to fair size in the water and then usually lose their gills and tail fins to emerge on land as true lung-breathing young, which continue growing until they attain a length of up to 12 inches.

Giant Pacific Salamander

Dicamptodon ensatus

In the damp Pacific coastal forests there are many kinds of salamanders, but none bigger than these. During a life history much like the *Ambystoma* they may attain a length of a foot or more, thus ranking as our largest land-dwelling species. In one instance one of these salamanders was seen eating a mouse which is rather a feat, considering that most salamanders live on tiny creatures and have difficulty swallowing a large earthworm!

Amphibians: Aquatic Salamanders

The Aquatic Salamanders

Congo "Eel"

Largest of our salamanders is the Congo "eel" or mud "eel," *Amphiuma*, which grows to over 3 feet in length. It lives in swamps of the lower Coastal Plain and is a strange creature, with legs so small they appear useless. People usually think it is an eel of some sort. It is a nocturnal, water-dwelling species but has lungs instead of gills and comes out on land now and then, particularly at breeding time. Its strings of jelly-enclosed eggs have been found under logs in mucky ground, guarded by the female.

Also of eel-like form are the sirens, *Siren* and *Pseudobranchus*, which have only front legs and branched, external gills at each side of the head. Several species are known which vary from little 6-inch forms, *P. striatus*, to one which may reach 3 feet in length, *S. lacertina*. These salamanders occur through the Coastal Plain up to Washington, D. C., and into the Central region to Lake Michigan.

"Mud puppy" or "water dog" are names given to a certain group of salamanders, *Necturus*, which never lose their gills and resemble the larval young of some other salamanders (see page 75). Different species vary from 5 to 18 inches in length, and their fluffy external gills and rather dog-shaped faces give them a more attractive appearance than some other forms shown here. Mud puppies occur generally in the Great Lakes, St. Lawrence, and Mississippi River systems and in certain rivers of the Atlantic and Gulf coasts.

Mud Puppy

Most salamanders get some oxygen through their skin, which is well supplied with mucous glands, but the hellbenders, *Cryptobranchus*, have extra equipment in this respect. The wrinkled, loose skin covering the whole animal amounts practically to a large gill surface. The creature is as slippery as wet soap. Two feet is the usual maximum length for these big, flat salamanders which are found in rocky streams in Appalachian, Central, and Ozark regions. Their eggs, like strings of large beads, are guarded by the males.

Hellbender

APPENDIX

Reptiles and Amphibians as Pets

Reptiles and amphibians do not make highly responsive pets as do dogs and cats, but some people find an interest in keeping and studying them. Although finding proper foods for them is often considerable trouble, they are for the most part good-natured animals and frequently become quite tame. In general, species native to the part of the country where you live are the wisest choice, for if they don't flourish in captive conditions they can be easily released in their natural habitat.

Glass aquariums with deep water are best suited to aquatic salamanders and the polliwog larval phase of other amphibians. Shallow-water aquariums with pieces of wood or stone (flowerpots split in half are excellent) for the creatures to crawl out on or hide under are satisfactory quarters for the small turtles, frogs, or alligators whose natural home is the water.

Terrariums are merely aquarium tanks containing a layer of soil or sand, a variety of ground plants, and a pan or shallow bowl of water. When covered with a piece of glass and placed away from the hot sun they are excellent for keeping the less aquatic frogs, tree frogs, toads, and most salamanders. When left open or covered with screen they are suitable for baby land turtles, small snakes, or lizards from moist habitats.

Lizards from desert regions do best in cages of hardware cloth (¼-inch mesh) or screen which let in plenty of sun and air. Flooring of fine dry sand is satisfactory for these lizards, but for many species water must be sprinkled into the cages daily for them to drink as they would raindrops. Some pieces of bark or flat stones should be placed in the cage for shelter.

One type of snake cage is a box of wood with large screened ventilators in the back and top and a sliding glass panel in the front. This should be about two thirds as long as the longest snake in the cage. Either newspaper or sand can be used on the floor and a bowl of fresh water should always be available to the reptile. The only other necessary object is a hiding place of bark, a hollow log, or an upside-down box with a hole in one side.

Outdoor pens and pools can of course be used to keep turtles, alligators, and frogs during the warmer months, but whether indoors or out, the temperatures to which the reptiles or amphibians are exposed are important. Too much hot sun or a chilling night may sicken or kill them. Generally speaking, amphibians need temperatures between 60° and 70° F., and reptiles between 70° and 80° to be comfortable and active.

INDEX

Michael H. Bevans, the talented author-illustrator of *The Book of Reptiles and Amphibians*, is an ardent naturalist. He lives in Tenafly, New Jersey, where he spends a great deal of his spare time in the outdoors, studying and painting his surroundings.

Mr. Bevans has done identification cards for the National Audubon Society, and his paintings have been featured in *Life* Magazine. In addition to this book, he was both the author and illustrator of *The Book of Sea Shells*.